BIRD KINGDOM OF THE MAYAS

BIRD
KINGDOM
OF THE
MAYAS

by
Ann LaBastille Bowes

illustrated by
Anita Benarde

D. VAN NOSTRAND COMPANY, INC.
Princeton, New Jersey   Toronto   London   Melbourne

Van Nostrand Regional Offices:

New York, Chicago, San Francisco

D. Van Nostrand Company, Ltd., London

D. Van Nostrand Company (Canada), Ltd., Toronto

D. Van Nostrand Australia Pty. Ltd., Melbourne

Published simultaneously in Canada by
D. Van Nostrand Company (Canada), Ltd.

Library of Congress Catalog Card No. 67-18066

PRINTED IN THE UNITED STATES OF AMERICA

Contents

How the King of the Birds Was Chosen

LONG ago, everything was different in the land of the Mayas. Flowers, birds, trees, and animals were dressed in different colors and shapes than those we see today. Halach-Uinic the Great Spirit guarded all Mayaland, and his rule was law.

One day the Great Spirit grew tired of the constant chatter and fighting among the birds. He decided to organize the bird kingdom so that order would rule. Calling for roadrunner, chief of the messengers, he sent word to all the birds to meet next day in the center of the forest. There they would choose a king of the birds—a strong ruler who would keep peace in the land.

Immediately each bird began to boast of his powers. Col-pol-che the cardinal sang, "Look at me! No one else is bright red and as beautiful as I. All the birds admire me. I should be king." And he strutted before his audience, fluttering his wings and raising his crest.

X-col-col-chek the mockingbird trilled, "I'm the only bird with such a lovely voice. Listen." Enlarging his throat, X-col gave a short concert of enchanting melody. This caused a great sensation among the birds and went far to convince them that the mockingbird should be king.

The wild turkey, Cutz, strode into the middle of the circle and gobbled, "There's no doubt that I should be your ruler. Am I not the strongest bird? With my size and strength, I can stop any fight and defend

any bird in trouble. You need a powerful king, and I'm the one!"

And so, on through the day the birds showed off their beauty or intelligence or strength or wisdom or skill.

But Kukul the quetzal bird remained quiet. He listened patiently to each bird tell why he should be king, but he did not dare to compete. Kukul was very ambitious and proud. He had fine manners and a graceful body, but his feathers were shabby and rather dull. The quetzal thought he could never be chosen king because he was dressed so poorly. Kukul watched the many contestants and thought about being king. Suddenly he had an idea. He flew over to his friend Xtun-tun-kinil the roadrunner, and said, "I would like to make you an offer, my dear fellow. Your feathers are as handsome as any bird's here, but you are too busy with your work as messenger to become king. And I don't think you have quite the flair and elegance that a king should have. I can't loan these qualities to you, but you can loan me your plumage just for this contest. When I am elected king, I'll share the wealth and honors with you."

Roadrunner was silent as he thought of the glory he would have if he were the closest friend to the new king. It was a tempting offer, but he did not care to part with his beautiful plumage. But Kukul kept talking and assuring Xtun-tun of his honesty and his good intentions. He painted bright pictures of the riches to come. At last the roadrunner was convinced, and he removed his feathers one by one and lent them to the clever quetzal who fixed them on his body as if they were his own.

Within minutes they had multiplied and grown so that the quetzal was dressed in the most splendid costume. Kukul's tail hung in a sweeping curve of jade green plumes. His body shimmered with soft blues and greens like the Mayan sky and jungle. His breast blazed with the red of a tropical sunset. Swinging his lovely long tail in an arc, the bold bird promenaded into the clearing where all the birds of Mayaland were assembled. His entrance caused a hush, and then cries of "Bravo," "Hurrah," "Oh," and "Ah" filled the forest. Some birds twitched their tails in envy, others squawked in surprise. There was not one who did not feel some jealousy at the sight of this beautiful new bird. Of course they did not recognize Kukul.

Halach-Uinic the Great Spirit was pleased. He called the crowd to order and declared, "I name the quetzal to be king of the birds."

A loud flapping of wings followed this announcement as each bird fluttered over to Kukul to offer congratulations. Then a big party was given in Kukul's honor, and after this all the birds flew home and left him to begin his new duties as king. Kukul found himself so busy that he had no time to return the borrowed plumes. In fact, he was afraid to take them off and soon forgot about his promise to the roadrunner.

One day a group of the birds was meeting in a Chacah, or gumbo limbo, tree. One of them noticed that Xtun-tun-kinil had not appeared. No one had seen him since the great election of the king. The birds then began to suspect that Kukul had played some kind of a trick and they immediately organized a search for the roadrunner.

At last, deep in the jungle behind a Zip-che, or coffee, bush, they found the road-runner naked and trembling with cold and half dead. Quickly, the birds gave him some balche, the sacred honey drink of the Mayas, to help him recover. As soon as he was able, Xtun-tun-kinil told them about the cruel trick played on him by the quetzal bird and he kept crying, "Where is he?

13

Where is he?" which sounds like, "Puhuy? Puhuy?" in Mayan language. The birds felt sorry for the roadrunner. They knew it would be impossible for him to get his feathers back now that Kukul was the king of the birds, so they decided that each would give a few plumes to cover the poor road-runner. While they were arranging all the different feathers on his body, mockingbird sang a jolly song to cheer him. That is why today roadrunner's plumage has so many colors and odd patterns and why he always can be found alongside the Mayan roads. He is still searching for the quetzal bird who took away his coat. He runs along in front of travelers asking, "Puhuy? Puhuy?— Where is he? Where is he?"

Why the Whippoorwill
Weeps and Wails

IN OLDEN times, Chak-puhuy the whippoorwill was a very quiet bird who flew about in the daytime. His one good feature was a coat of pretty feathers—gold, purple, and bronze. Chak was all good looks *outside* and nothing *inside* his head.

On the day the birds were called together for the election of their king, the whippoorwill was sitting next to Cutz the wild turkey. Cutz wanted to go in front of the audience and explain why he should be king, but he was ashamed of his plumage.

Turning to the whippoorwill, he said softly, "Your feathers are so beautiful. Will you let me borrow a few before I go before the crowd? I'm sure to be elected ruler if I look as handsome as I am strong and big."

Dumb little Chak-puhuy admired the turkey for his size and strength. Indeed, of all his wishes, he most wanted to be like Cutz. So he willingly gave the turkey all the plumes he wanted. One by one, the large bird arranged them until his tail spread out wide and shiny, and his wings shone like bronze in the sun.

Cutz made his speech and strutted to show how beautiful and strong he was, but the quetzal was chosen king instead. The turkey was so upset at not winning, that he flapped away into the jungle and hid there for several days. He forgot all about the generous whippoorwill. In fact, he never thought of Chak again.

The poor bird had no friends so there

was no one to tell about his trouble or to help him. Slowly, sadly, Chak started looking on the forest floor and found a few old feathers along the paths and under trees. These he put on to cover himself, and to make his wings work again. They looked so dirty and frayed that Chak was ashamed to come out by day anymore. He would venture out only at dusk and sit by the roadside where it was easier to catch insects with his worn wings.

That is why today the whippoorwill appears only after dark, and why he always cries, "Puhuy? Puhuy?" just as the roadrunner does. They are looking for the selfish birds who stole their pretty feathers long ago. Chak-puhuy has wept so much that his eyes have turned red. If you shine a light on him at night, you can see his eyes glow as red as hot coals in the moment before he flies away.

Bech,
The Ambitious Quail

IN THE early days, Bech the quail was a pet of Halach-Uinic the Great Spirit. She wore soft feathers and a curly crest like a crown on top of her head. Her voice was gentle and she had good manners. The Great Spirit wanted to protect Bech from all harm so he allowed her to build her nest and raise her babies high in the treetops. There they would be safe from Indian hunters, wild animals, and snakes. Since she was never in danger Bech was able to raise a large and happy family every year.

Any other bird would have been content with such a safe life, but not Bech. She was forever dreaming of becoming queen of the birds. While she was sitting on her nest and flying about in the forest her mind was busy with schemes to become the queen.

One morning a large band of Mayan hunters crept through the jungle on the trail of a wild turkey. They were seeking a large turkey cock with plenty of meat on its bones, for turkey meat is a favorite dish of the Indians. The hunters had tracked Cutz a long way, but they had not been able to shoot because Cutz kept sneaking ahead through the brush and would not fly. He knew that as long as he stayed on the ground he was safe from arrows and stones.

But in time Cutz grew tired. He saw a small cave ahead in the rocks, and he headed straight for it. He squeezed inside to hide from his pursuers while he rested. Bech, meanwhile, was watching the hunt

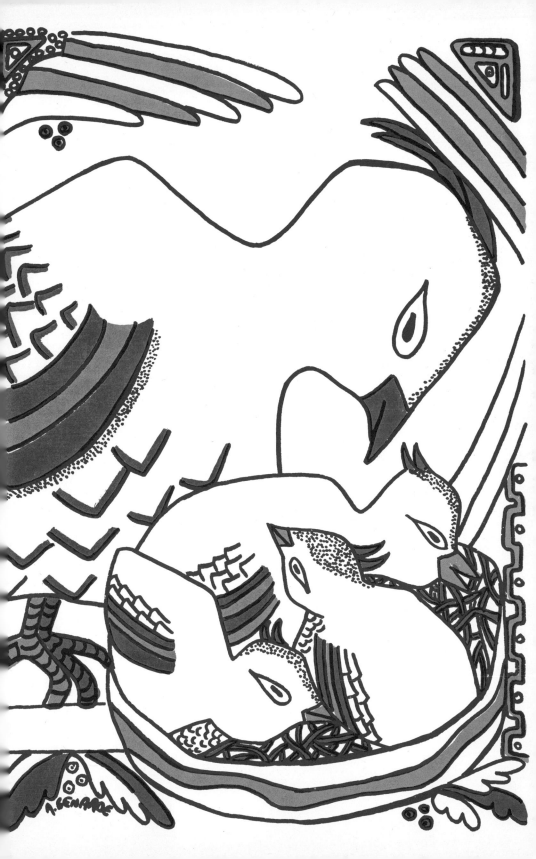

from her nest in the treetop. When she saw that the Indians had lost Cutz and were about to give up the chase, she flew down and made a strange noise near the cave where the wild turkey was hiding. The hunters ran to see what the noise was, found Cutz's hiding place, and at once they snared the poor cock with ropes and vines. Also watching the hunt were Mutz the green frog and Sitam the peccary. These two animals knew Bech had betrayed the turkey cock, so they dashed up to Bech and scolded her. Both warned that the Great Spirit would be angry at her cruel deed.

"Why should the Great Spirit be annoyed if I help humans?" asked the mean little quail. "Those Indians might help me to become queen someday, and that is my greatest wish."

Bech soon learned that Halach-Uinic *was* very angry with her, indeed. He knew that his beloved pet had been a traitor to the birds and in this she had deeply hurt him. The Great Spirit knew that he would have to punish Bech. He dried the tears from his eyes and decided on the punishment.

He called all the birds together and announced, "From now on, Bech, you and your family and all quails to come will not be protected by me. You must live in the grasses where many other birds live and take your chances against the hunters and wild animals. Never again will you live safely high in the treetops. From this time on you will have to look out for yourself."

And to this day, quails live close to the ground. They still have large families, but many are captured by the hunters or by the wild animals of the jungle.

The Woodpecker
and the Jade Stone

IN THE early days of the bird kingdom
there lived an old Indian, Rex-habaj,
who was known as the best hunter in all
Mayaland. Birds and animals alike respected this man because he never hunted
for fun, never killed unless his people
needed meat or skins, and never hurt the
wild creatures or left them in pain. The
Indians also admired this hunter because he
made fine weapons, always hit his mark,
and always returned safely from the hunt.

The secret of his success was a small jade
stone which his father had given him, and

his father before that, back to the most ancient times. This gem was believed to give a hunter the best luck in the world.

One day when the old hunter went into the jungle, he found the tracks of a huge jaguar. They were the largest tracks he had ever seen. Eagerly, he followed the footprints. He said to himself, "I will track Balam the jaguar and see where he sleeps. Then I can return with better weapons and more hunters to catch him. His coat will make a fine robe for our chief, and his teeth a beautiful necklace for the princess."

Rex-habaj tracked Balam all day. In one hand, he carried his brown blowgun and, in the other, a bag of round stones. At dusk, he began to draw closer to the jaguar. That part of the jungle was full of rocks. As the hunter crept through a narrow pass, he suddenly found himself right behind the animal. Trembling with excitement, Rex-habaj grabbed a stone from his bag, pushed it into the blowgun and shot at the big cat to scare him away. To his amazement, the stone missed its mark and flew high into the trees where it hit a large woodpecker. Rex-habaj was so surprised and frightened that he ran away before Balam had time to jump.

When the hunter returned to his village, he was very upset. It was the first time he had ever failed. He searched for his lucky stone in all his clothing, but it had disap-peared. Then he realized that he must have put the jade piece in the blowgun by mis-take. Rex-habaj went back to the tree where he had shot at Balam and looked all over the ground for the woodpecker, but there was no bird and no feathers. "That bird must have my lucky gem," thought the Indian. "How can I get it back?" And from that day, he did nothing but search for Colonte the flintbill, largest woodpecker in the forest. Rex-habaj lost his skill as a mighty hunter and his good fortune, too. But Colonte had luck finding food, trees to perch in, and safe nests.

So the legend grew in Mayaland that the woodpecker guarded the stone well under his right wing. If anyone killed him for the jade, bad luck would fall upon that hunter. Yet only that person who possessed the precious stone would ever become a great hunter. For years many men tried to get it back, but no one succeeded.

In the same village, there lived a young boy, Tziquin. His father had died long ago, and Tziquin lived alone with his mother and two dogs. Tziquin showed early in life that he was a true friend of the forest. He knew the songs of all the birds, could tell the uses of plants and flowers for medicine and food, could run as fast as a deer, and climbed as well as the monkeys. Many people believed he would be a fine hunter someday, so the men of the village took time to teach Tziquin how to swim, shoot, make arrows and blowguns, and to track animals.

Tziquin's mother, wishing only the best for her son, often thought about Rex- habaj's jade stone. Sometimes, while she was cooking in front of a little fire, or at night, when they were swinging to sleep in their hammocks, she would talk to Tziquin about the woodpecker and his gem. They made many plans to trap the bird, but al- ways there was the problem of how to keep him from harm. Finally, the mother hit upon a clever plan.

They waited until spring when Yum- Chac the rain god began to prepare his storms. As the first rains fell, Colonte and his wife started looking for a good tree to nest in. It was important to find a large tree with soft wood so that a hole could be carved inside. There, the female would line the nest with wood fibers and chips and lay her eggs.

Tziquin wandered all over the jungle

until he saw a huge tree, Nim-majche by name, with a big, oval hole high up on its trunk. "Colonte must live there," thought the boy. "I will watch." So he hid under some palm leaves and waited. In a few hours, both birds flew out of the hole and away into the forest to look for food.

The Indian lad climbed the huge tree and sealed over the hole with branches and bark. When the woodpeckers returned to feed their babies, they found the doorway was blocked. Angrily, Colonte hammered at the trunk and made a new opening. Next day, Tziquin hid again under the tree and when the birds left, he climbed up and closed the entrance. Once more, the woodpeckers had to drill a new hole. This went on for nine days, and poor Tziquin was bruised and scratched from climbing so often up the tall tree. The birds were tired, too. Never before had they worked so hard to enter their nest.

On the ninth day, as Colonte hammered out a new hole the jade stone dropped from under his wing. Tziquin dashed up, snatched up the stone, and ran home to his mother. Everyone in the village was astounded and very proud of the young boy. "Now you will certainly be the best hunter in Mayaland," said the chief. "Hereafter we will call you Tziquin-Nim-majche, or Little Bird of the Mighty Tree."

31

The Cardinal's Concert

ONE winter, during the dry season, a famous professor of singing came to Mayaland. His name was Dr. Xcau, the melodious blackbird, and his reputation was excellent. Immediately, the cardinal decided that his daughter Col-pol-che should become a fine singer. He called Col-pol-che to him and explained his idea to her. But the lazy girl shook her head and refused. She said she was not interested in becoming a fine singer. Her father insisted, but Col-pol-che just grew more and more sullen. Finally she flew away into the forest to join her girl friends.

32

X-col-col-chek the mockingbird had overheard father cardinal talking with his
daughter, and saw her fly away from the
wonderful opportunity to study singing.
"How unfair life is!" she thought to herself.
"Here I am anxious to learn to sing, but I
can't afford a single lesson. Yet Col-pol-che
is given the chance and she throws it away."
Poor X-col-col-chek sighed, and went on
about her duties as the cardinal's maid serv-
ant.

That evening when Col-pol-che returned
home, both of her parents urged her to go
to the professor to learn to sing. They promised her many gifts if only she would try. At
last the lazy Col-pol-che agreed. Next morning she went with Dr. Xcau to a quiet part
of the woods and began her music lesson.

Unknown to both birds, X-col-col-chek
followed behind and hid in the bushes in
order to listen and learn from the professor.
For weeks the professor tried to teach Col-

pol-che to sing sweetly, but he had no success. He soon realized that she possessed
neither the interest nor the voice to do so.
Yet having accepted so much money from
his pupil's wealthy father, he did not wish
to admit his lack of success at teaching her
to sing. At last Dr. Xcau decided to fly away
and forget the whole affair.

Meanwhile the mockingbird was prac-
ticing all she had overheard. When the
cardinal's nest was empty or she was gather-
ing berries in the jungle, X-col-col-chek
would trill and warble. One morning Col-
pol-che happened to come home unexpect-
edly and heard the mockingbird's beautiful
singing. She and her friends circled quietly
down and hid nearby in a Kuy-che tree. Col-
pol-che was amazed at the little maid's ability.

The same day, father cardinal decided
that his daughter had had enough lessons
to be ready to give a concert for their

friends. Without bothering to ask the professor, he began to invite the guests and to choose a space in the forest where the concert could take place. That evening he told Col-pol-che that she should prepare her repertoire.

The lazy girl was terrified, but she did not dare tell her father that she couldn't sing after all the lessons she had had. Instead, she flew to find Dr. Xcau and told him of her plight. He, too, was horrified, for he thought it would not speak well for him if it was discovered that after all his lessons his pupil still could not sing. Instead of helping the cardinal, he flew swiftly away to a different part of the land where no one would hear of this misfortune. Col-pol-che frantically tried to get help from her playmates, but they were all too stupid or lazy to care. She thought of the mockingbird's lovely voice and decided to ask her for help.

The two birds plotted in this way: They

would ask Colonte the woodpecker to bore a hole into the tree trunk where Col-pol-che was supposed to perch. Then, just before the performance, the mockingbird would creep inside the hole and hide. When the cardinal pretended to be singing, the real voice would come from X-col-col-chek behind her.

On the night of the concert all the nobles, singers, artists, and musicians among the birds came to hear the cardinal. It was a big social event. The cardinal's father had chosen a purple flowering tree as the music stand. And he had many musicians clustered below it to accompany his daughter. Dressed in his sleekest red suit and with his large beak shined and polished, he felt like the proudest father in all the bird kingdom. Cardinal hopped out onto the limb, bowed to the audience, and then the most exquisite voice ever heard in Mayaland came forth echoing through the trees. The audience was so enraptured that they flapped their wings and cried for more and more songs. Every guest showed great admiration for the young bird's voice.

The cardinal's father, however, was not applauding. Just the moment before the concert began he had noticed the hole behind the perch, and had seen the mockingbird slip inside. He realized that it was not his daughter who was singing so sweetly, but their drab little maid—the mockingbird.

When the applause had ended and Col-pol-che had taken many bows, her father flew up beside her and asked for silence. He hopped to the hole and called to X-col-col-chek to come out. The poor little gray bird was trembling with fright at being caught, but the father cardinal's quiet voice gave her courage. When she appeared he announced the truth to the audience. His daughter had tricked everyone. "*This* shy little nightingale is the bird who sang during tonight's concert," he explained.

Then the crowd went wild and demanded that X-col-col-chek sing again. This time, free from her hiding place and her fears, X-col-col-chek sang as never before and won every bird's heart. From that time to this, all her descendants have inherited this beautiful singing voice, but cardinals have never learned to sing.

Ani,
The Mother Who Was Too Proud

LONG ago, Chick-bul the ani was a pretty pink bird. But, even more important, she was a good, loving mother. She adored all her babies and worked hard to keep them well and happy. The ani's best friend was a small hawk called Canan-col. These two birds spent much time together, chatting, eating, and flying around the forest.

Chick-bul knew that her friend the hawk liked to eat tiny birds for dessert, although most of the time she was content with snakes, rats, and frogs. When the ani's first

brood of babies was born, she asked Canan-col not to eat them by mistake. The hawk promised to be careful. Chick-bul described her nest and young chicks, and like any proud mother, she believed hers were the most beautiful babies in the bird kingdom. She warned the hawk that her nest was in an Azar, the white acacia tree, and again Canan-col promised to be careful.

One morning, however, the hawk awoke feeling terribly hungry. It seemed that the only thing which would satisfy her craving was a nestful of tiny chicks. Canan-col began to hunt early. Flying over an Azar tree, she spied a nest of white, fuzzy, little birds. She swooped lower and saw that they were fat, juicy, and tender. In fact, they were so pretty that the hawk thought they must be the ani's children. True to her word, she did not harm them.

Flying on through the forest, Canan-col caught a few lizards, a big insect, a small snake, but her appetite for baby birds still remained. Toward noon, she grew tired and flew into another Azar tree. While she was resting, she heard some tiny peeps near the lowest branch. The hawk hopped down and found a small nest with six, scrawny, ugly chicks. They were so skinny that Canan-col thought they would make a very poor dessert, but she gobbled them up. Then she went back to rest.

That afternoon, Chick-bul returned to her nest, carrying seeds and caterpillars for her brood. As she fluttered down through the Azar tree, she saw with horror her empty home. The feathers from her babies were scattered all around. Shrieking with grief, she pulled at her own feathers and cursed Canan-col. "What a traitor my best friend turned out to be. Canan-col has broken her promise and eaten all my children."

Chick-bul leaped into the air and set out to find the hawk. She searched through those parts of the jungle where Canan-col liked to sleep and finally found her dozing in a tree. "You traitor! Monster!" screamed the ani. "You lied. My babies are dead!"

The hawk woke up with a fright to see her little pink friend in such a rage. In fact, she had to protect herself from the attacks of the distraught mother. "Chick-bul, Chick-bul," she squawked, "I kept my word. I did not eat your babies. I found your six, pretty, white birdlets in an Azar tree and I left them alone. They never even had a glimpse of me to scare them. I only ate six skinny runts that I found later. They couldn't have been *your* babies."

Then Chick-bul realized how much she must have exaggerated about her children, as all mothers like to do. She dragged herself sadly home, pulled out all her pink plumes and put on black, mourning feathers. To this day, all anis wear black feathers and twitch their tails back and forth in grief.

44

Why Owls See Only at Night

IN THE kingdom of the birds, there were noble birds, crooked birds, mean birds, stupid and wise birds. Usually, the wise ones were the owls, and they had the job of advising the king. Because of their serious habits, owls were greatly respected by all birds. They spent much time studying. Their eyes were so sharp that they could read and see clearly both day and night.

One day, Kukul, king of the birds, wanted to have a big fiesta. He ordered the musical birds—thrushes, tanagers, orioles, blackbirds, and mockingbirds—to play. He asked for dancing birds—manakins, banana-

45

quits, sandpipers, and honeycreepers—to perform. He called for the hummingbirds to bring fresh flowers and for the woodpeckers to decorate the trees. Then, he wrote invitations and sent for his messengers—the roadrunners, falcons, swallows, and kites. They were to give notice to every bird in Mayaland. King Kukul urged his messengers to make sure that *all* birds were invited so the party would be a large, gay affair.

When Ikim the horned owl received his invitation, he shook his head, No. The messenger, Chuy the swallowtailed kite advised the owl to come so that King Kukul would not be sorry. Ikim refused, muttering that deep studies were keeping him busy. Chuy kept urging the owl, and finally he agreed.

The day of the great fiesta came, sunny, bright, and cool. From all parts of the jungle, the birds of Mayaland flew in. They were dressed in the finest of feathers and on their best behavior. Balche, the holy honey drink

46

of the Mayas, was served in small golden goblets. Each glass was made so that birds could dip their beaks inside easily.

In a short while, every bird except Ikim was enjoying the music, the songs, dancing, and delicious drinks. Most of them, in fact, became very jolly. King Kukul, however, saw that his wise adviser Ikim would not drink anything, and that he sat glumly in a corner. The royal bird hopped over and began a song. Owl merely dropped his eyelids and paid no attention.

The king flew into a rage and swooped upon Ikim. "Why don't you look at me?" he screeched. "The other guests are flapping their wings and chirping. Why can't *you* enjoy my party?"

The sad old bird answered solemnly, "I am too smart and too serious a bird to enjoy this foolishness. I have much work to do with my books. I want to go home."

Furious, King Kukul told owl to go to the

48

center of the stage. "Now you will sing and dance *alone* to please me and to make up for your bad manners!" he commanded.

The poor owl was so clumsy and had such a hoarse voice that he gave a silly show. All the guests laughed and whooped at him. Deeply insulted and ashamed, Ikim flew quickly away to his dark cave.

He hid there for many days, reading old and mystical books. He was searching for a revenge. After weeks of study, he found an ancient tale which told of the foul trick played by the first king of birds. It told how he stole the beautiful feathers of roadrunner and never gave them back, so that the poor bird almost died naked and cold. This story about the first quetzal king gave owl an idea.

Next day, he called a meeting of noble birds outside his cave. When everyone was perched around his door, Ikim came out with an old, old book bound in deer hide and filled with pages of papyrus. Owl began, "Oh, Maya birds, I am going to tell you a story that you should know." Standing in the bright sun, he began to read the tale.

Suddenly, his eyes began to hurt. The more he read, the weaker and fuzzier the print became. Black dots danced over the pages. Tears came to his eyes and fell to the ground. Ikim had read only a short part of the story when he became blind. The glare of light on the pages after having spent so many days in his dark cave was too much for his eyes. Thus, owl was not able to finish the story and the nobles left, shaking their heads in confusion. They never found out that the first king had been a liar and a thief.

In partial punishment for his bad manners and his vengeful nature, the Great Spirit made the owl blind by day. That is why most owls hide quietly in gloomy places during the day and become active only at night when they can see.

The Story of Cozumel,
The Lazy Swallow

YEARS ago when the birds were new on earth, they looked much different than they do today. Cozumel the swallow was a dazzling bright bird with a slender forked tail and swift flight. He was so graceful that all the gods admired him. They decided to make him their chief messenger. In this high position, swallow was permitted to sit beside the Great Spirit and to carry the royal news of the bird kingdom. The other birds respected Cozumel because of his job, but they all knew that he was lazy and vain.

In the spring when birds were building their nests everywhere in Mayaland, the swallow was still at work carrying messages. In his free time, Cozumel and his wife would fly over pools of water, chase butterflies, look at flowers, and relax. They never thought of making a nest, but instead, used other birds' homes whenever they wished. No one dared chase Cozumel away because of his important position.

Soon, however, the birds grew angry with his nest-squatting. They went in a group to the Great Spirit and asked that he make swallow build his own nest. Halach-Uinic thought for awhile and then sent for Cozumel and his wife.

"Since you have been busy carrying my messages every day," he said kindly, "you may not have had time to learn about building a nest. But now is the time when each bird must prepare a safe, warm home for his babies. You may have a vacation and

pick any bird you wish to be your teacher. Let him show you how to build your own home."

Many birds were willing to help Cozumel. X-col-col-chek the mockingbird told how to pick up dry grasses and twigs to use at the base of the nest. Before she had even finished explaining, Cozumel said smugly, "I know, I know."

Then Yuyum the oriole showed swallow how to weave pieces of vine, animal hair, tough grasses, and bark fibers into a hanging nest that would swing in the wind. Cozumel quickly said, "I know, I know."

Thinking that Cozumel's wife might show more interest, Tzunuum the hummingbird, most fragile of birds, showed her how to gather lichens and pluck soft down from her breast so as to form a cosy little cup nest. The swallow also answered lazily, "I know, I know."

Even Ya the flycatcher tried. He thought

54

his method of finding a hole in a tree and lining it with soft materials might be easier for the swallows. But, again, they paid no attention.

The time came when all the birds had nice nests in which their eggs were lying, waiting to hatch. Only the swallows were homeless. Cozumel's wife tried to sneak her eggs into other birds' nests, but this time she was chased away. Then, she tried to build her own place. It fell apart under the weight of her first egg. The second one blew down in an evening wind. Sadly, she begged her husband to go back to mockingbird and learn the right way to build a nest. But by this time the lovely songster was too busy with her babies to bother. She told Cozumel to come back later. The frightened swallows then asked Yuyum, Tzunuum, and Ya, but they were also too busy.

Crying in sorrow because her babies would die without a warm nest, Cozumel's wife flew to a large cenote, a Mayan well, and perched at the edge. Between sobs, she heard a tiny voice coming from down inside the well. Peering over the edge, she saw a wasp clinging to a slippery leaf. It was struggling against falling in the water and drowning.

Cozumel's wife chirped out, "What will you give me to save your life?"

"Anything!" gasped Xux the wasp.

The swallow flitted gracefully into the cenote and passed close to the insect. "Will you show me how to make a nest?"

"Yes," cried the tired creature, so the swallow picked him gently from the leaf and flew up to the edge again. True to his word, the grateful wasp took grass and mud and packed it against the cenote wall to form a nest. The swallow said it looked too ugly for messengers of the Great Spirit. "We need a large and fine home," she grumbled.

Xux, however, knew no other way of making a nest. He told her that this style was fine enough for a queen. Being such a vain bird, Cozumel's wife was pleased with this thought. Besides, she was too ashamed to ask any more birds for help.

So, she and her husband went to work and built their nest the same way that wasps do. Instead of using trees like most birds, they stuck bits of clay and mud to the walls of caves, cenotes, and Mayan houses or chozas. The other birds laughed at their funny-looking home, but the swallows knew no other way of building a nest. Still, to this day, nesting swallows copy the wasps, as proof of their lazy and vain life in the past.

How Vanity
Made the Dove Sad

EVERY morning in Mayaland, the birds are wakened by the sad song of Mucuy the ground dove. She is one of the unhappiest of birds, yet she has no one to blame but herself for her sorrow.

Long ago, Mucuy wore very ugly plumage. Her feathers were a dull, brown color, all worn and shabby, but her flight was as swift and as graceful as the swallow. Mucuy hated her dress and every day she would go to a nearby cenote and gaze at her reflection.

"How drab I am," she would sigh. "Why did the Great Spirit make me so ugly?"

Halach-Uinic heard her unhappy cries and called Mucuy up for a talk. He explained that each bird had some feature that was not pleasing, but also that each one had a special skill or beauty which he could be proud of. The little ground dove hung her head, trying to listen. She was so shy and confused before the powerful god that she could not understand anything.

The Great Spirit said, "Your best feature is not your feathers, Mucuy, but remember how well you can fly."

Mucuy broke out, crying, "Many birds are prettier than I. Little hummingbird is like a rainbow, and she flies backward *and* forward. Yuyum the oriole wears the yellow of sunrises; and Col-pol-che the cardinal, the red of sunsets. X-chel the jay looks like the bluest of skies, and Toj the motmot has all the colors of a cenote. But, me—I'm like mud!"

When Halach-Uinic realized how bitter

the ground dove was, he felt sorry for her. "I will change your feathers, if you will help me with some work," he promised.

Next day, the Great Spirit told all the birds that an extra messenger was needed to help Cozumel. Mucuy would take the job in return for a new dress of feathers. The birds agreed at once because everyone liked sweet Mucuy. Each gave her one plume and soon the little dove was dressed in the prettiest coat of soft colors. Some shades were like the pale rays of sun after rain. Others were like the rose and white of early morning clouds. Still others had hues of lavender and mauve. Mucuy became the happiest bird in the kingdom. She flew right away to the cenote to admire her new appearance.

A short time later, there came an election for the next king of the birds. Mucuy was ordered to carry messages to each bird chief, telling of the meeting. She tied the notes to her legs and flew off with every good in-

tention. Her flight took her over a clear, calm cenote. Since it was a bright, sunny day with perfect reflections in the water, she flapped down to look at herself. The vain bird spent all morning admiring her beautiful feathers, and forgot to deliver the messages.

When Hohoch Kin the sun god came to the center of the heavens, Mucuy was still strutting, turning, bowing, and showing off to herself. The Great Spirit, meanwhile, was waiting anxiously for the bird chiefs in answer to his important notes. Hohoch Kin covered the whole sky, and still no birds appeared. The Great Spirit became angry and shouted for the grackles, his guardians of the court, to go and check. These black birds flew speedily away and soon found Mucuy preening at the edge of the well. They ordered her to go back to the king.

Obedience was the highest law of Halach-Uinic. He brought Mucuy before him for punishment. The ground dove was so frightened that she stood with her head hanging down to the ground and her wings a-tremble. "You have broken my faith in you," roared Halach-Uinic. "My messages are serious business, yet there they are still tied to your legs. You must be punished."

The Great Spirit continued, "I will not take away your fine new feathers, but I will remove your power of fast high flight. From now on, Mucuy, you are no longer my messenger. You will stay close to the ground with Mulzay the ant, Kan the snake, Zadz the worm, and Sinaan the scorpion. You will never fly swiftly or high again!"

Next morning when Mucuy tried to spring into the sky and see out over the forest and fields, she could not do it. She could fly only in short stretches low over the ground and the cenotes. Now she could spend as long as she wanted gazing at herself in the water, but she could not travel anywhere. Sadly, she cried, "Aku, aku— Poor me, poor me."

And since that time, so long ago, all ground doves have been unhappy, uttering their mournful cry in the early morning.

Why the Motmot Lives
in a Hole

ONE of the royal birds who lived during the time of the early bird kingdom looked almost as beautiful as King Kukul. He had a long, shiny, fragile tail of many colors which all the birds admired. Toj the motmot was so proud of it that he never did any work which might harm the feathers. Instead, this lazy creature flew into the cool jungle with his noble friends and spent the entire day there, preening, telling jokes, and eating. At noon, Toj and his friends might enjoy a light lunch of insects or lizards. During the afternoon, they would sip drops of dew still left from nighttime. Always, Motmot would coax his friends to bring food to his branch so as not to harm his tail.

One noon, black clouds began to gather over Mayaland. All the trees looked sad and stopped whispering. They hung their leaves and shivered. Animals darted nervously about, looking for shelter. The insects stopped humming and buzzing. A strange hush filled the forest and it looked as though a terrible storm were about to burst.

Yum Chac the rain god was joyful. Now he could come down from the skies where he had spent the dry winter months. He could travel with the rain and explore many cenotes, rivers, and lakes. As he was planning his fun, he suddenly remembered that one of his fierce storms had made a flood. Much of Mayaland had been covered with water and many birds and animals were killed. Yum Chac grew worried. He thought

that his new storm might do the same sort of damage.

At once, he called an emergency meeting of the birds and explained the danger. He made a plan for safety and gave each bird a task to do in case of floods.

Chujut and Colonte, the woodpeckers, were to cut logs, while Panchel the toucan, Mox the macaw, and Exikin the parrot would break branches for a dam. Then, Bach the chachalaca and Cutz the wild turkey would lift and carry the heavy limbs. The grackles, orioles, and finches could weave grasses and twigs around them to make it watertight. The swift messengers, Xtun-tun-kinil the roadrunner, Mucuy the ground dove, and Cozumel the swallow were to watch the roads, cenotes, and skies to warn passersby of the danger. Birds who lived close to the ground, Bech the quail, Col-pol-che the cardinal, and many warblers and sparrows were given the job of collecting fruits, nuts, and seeds. This way, the birds would have something to eat and the forest could be replanted if floods destroyed the land. The chief of all these birds was Oc the vulture.

The only one who complained about the hard work was motmot. "I'm a noble," he grumbled. "I'm not a workman."

The other birds told Toj how sorry he would feel if the storm ruined Mayaland, and they urged the motmot to help. Scowling, the elegant bird took his place among the dam-builders. After a few minutes' work, he was tired and sweaty since he was not used to hard work. Toj waited until no one was watching, then sneaked off into the brush.

He found a dark nook and stretched himself out to sleep. Thinking he was well hidden, he did not notice that his tail was sticking out over a trail where the workers were walking with their loads.

Hours later, motmot woke up and heard the birds singing. The storm had blown over without much harm. The entire bird kingdom was rejoicing at their good fortune. Motmot crept out and flew to the dam. He asked everyone if they felt as tired as he did after the hard, long job. Each bird agreed that he was tired, but that the labor had been worthwhile to save the jungle and all its wildlife from disaster.

Then, some of the royal birds called to Toj and they flew to their favorite spot in the forest. Motmot, as usual, perched on a branch above the others so they might admire his handsome tail. Each bird began cleaning and preening his feathers.

Suddenly, one bird started to laugh, then another. Soon the whole group was roaring with amusement. They all pointed at Toj and said, "Your tail is spoiled. You must have ruined it with your hard work at the dam."

Motmot was sure they were joking until he peered down and saw two naked shafts sticking out of his body. There were only two spots of feathers left at each tip.

To his horror, he guessed what must have happened—while he slept the passing workers had trampled over his tail feathers. The lazy bird realized the damaged tail was his own fault, but he was too proud to let his friends learn the truth. Hot with shame and remorse, the motmot flapped away into the deepest, dimmest part of the jungle. There, he dug a hole in a bank and crawled inside. To this day, he has remained a forest hermit who shuns other birds and makes his home in a hole.

The Gift to the Hummingbird

TZUNUUM the hummingbird was created by the Great Spirit to be a tiny bird with marvellous flying ability. Tzunuum is the only bird in the kingdom who can fly backward as well as forward, and who can hover in one spot for several minutes. Because of this, the hummingbird is permitted to drink the nectar from flowers because she can sip it out without having to perch on or grab at the delicate blossoms.

In the beginning, Tzunuum was very

72

proud of her aerial agility. Even though her feathers were dull and plain, she was happy with her skill. The hummingbird never complained, but enjoyed life despite her poor looks.

When it came time to be married, Tzu-nuum realized she was not dressed well enough. Furthermore, she had neither a gown nor a necklace since clothes were the last things she ever thought about in her busy days. The hummingbird grew very sad and quiet, but she said nothing. Some friends wondered at her sadness at this time when she should have been radiant. Because they knew her well they suspected the cause and decided to give her a wedding outfit as a surprise.

Ya the vermilion-crowned flycatcher used to wear a gay crimson-red band of feathers about his throat in the early days of the bird kingdom. He placed a few of these bright tufts in his crown and gave the

rest to Tzunuum for her marriage necklace.

Uchichil the bluebird generously donated many blue feathers for her gown. The vain motmot came in from his jungle haunts, and, not to be outdone, gave more feathers of turquoise, green, and brown. The cardinal family contributed red ones. Yuyum the oriole was an excellent tailor as well as a nesting engineer, so he sewed all the feathers into an intricate and lovely wedding dress.

Ah-leum the spider crept up with a fragile veil woven of shiny gossamer threads. She helped oriole weave these designs into the dress and train. Canac the honey bee heard of the goings-on, and since he and all his clan liked the hummingbird and shared flowers with her, they brought much honey and nectar for the wedding reception. They persuaded the wasps and dragonflies to bring blossoms of flowers which the bees knew to be Tzunuum's favorites.

The Azar tree dropped a carpet of petals over the ground where the ceremony was to take place, and she offered to let the hummingbird and her groom spend their honeymoon in those sweet-smelling branches. Pakal the orange tree and Nicte the plumeria put forth fragrant flowers to perfume the forest. Haaz the banana bush, Op the custard apple tree, and Pichi and Put, the guava and papaya bushes, made certain that their fruits would be ripe and juicy for the wedding guests. And, finally, a large group of butterflies arrived to dance and flutter around the ritual and reception.

When the wedding day dawned and all these surprises were made known to Tzunuum, she was so happy and grateful she could barely twitter. Up to the very last moment, this humble bird had vowed to be married in her plain, shabby suit, wearing only a beautiful love in her heart. The Great Spirit admired her honest, simple soul so much that he sent word down to the festival with Cozumel the swallow. He told the hummingbird that she could wear her beautiful gown and necklace for the rest of her life. And to this day, all hummingbirds have.

Guide to Pronunciation

Azar (ah-zar) white acacia tree
Ah-leum (ah lee um) the spider

Bach (bahk) the chachalaca
Balam (bah lam) the jaguar
Balche (bahl chey) honey drink
Bech (beck) the quail

Canac (kah nak) the honeybee
Canan-col (kan an kol) the hawk
cenote (see no tey) well
Chacah (chah cah) gumbo-limbo tree
Chak-puhuy (chock poo hew) the whippoorwill
Chick-bul (chick bul) the ani
Chujut (chew hut) a woodpecker
Chuy (chewy) the swallowtailed kite
copal (ko pal) incense
Colonte (kol on tey) the flintbill woodpecker
Col-pol-che (kol pōl che) the cardinal's daughter
Cozumel (coz um el) the swallow
Cutz (kutz) the wild turkey

Exikin (esh i kin) the parrot

78

Haaz (haas) the banana bush
Halach-Uinic (ha lak u nic) the Great Spirit
Hohoch kin (ho hoch kin) the sun god

Ikim (eye kem) the horned owl

Kan (kahn) the snake
Kukul (koo kul) the quetzel

Mayaland (my ya land)
Mayas (my yas)
Mox (mush) the macaw
Mucuy (moo chew) the ground dove
Mulzay (muls ay) the ant
Mutz (muts) the green frog

Nicte (nic tay) plumeria
Nim-majche (nim mah chey) a huge tree
Op (ŏp) custard apple tree
Oc (ŏc) the vulture

Pakal (pāk al) orange tree
Panchel (pan chel) the toucan
Pichi (pee chee) guava
Put (pŭt) papaya
puhuy? (poo hew) Where is he?

Rex-habaj (Rex habah)

Sinaan (sin an) the scorpion
Sitam (sit am) the peccary

79

Toj (tōge) the motmot
Tziquin (zeekin) boy's name
Tziquin-Nim-majche (zeekin nem mah chey)
    Little Bird of the Mighty Tree
Tzunuum (zoo nuum) the hummingbird

Uchichil (u chi cheel) the bluebird

Xcau (sh-cow) the blackbird
X-chel (sh-chel) the jay bird
X-col-col-chek (sh col col chek) the mockingbird
Xtun-tun-kinil (sh tun tun ke nel) the roadrunner
Xux (shush) the wasp

Ya (yah) the flycatcher
Yum-Chac (yum-chac) the rain god
Yuyum (you yum) the oriole

Zadz (zads) the worm
Zipche (zip chey) coffee bush